Inference Jones

Beginning 2

Using Higher-Order Thinking to Improve Critical Reading and Comprehension

Inference Jones products available in print or eBook form.

Beginning 1 • Beginning 2 • Level 1

Written by
Robert E. Owen, M.A.

Graphic Design by
Annette Langenstein

Edited by
Susan Penfield
Catherine Connors-Nelson

© 2020, 2015, 2012
THE CRITICAL THINKING CO.™
www.CriticalThinking.com
Phone: 800-458-4849 • Fax: 541-756-1758
1991 Sherman Ave., Suite 200 • North Bend • OR 97459
ISBN 978-1-60144-451-6

MIX
Paper from
responsible sources
FSC® C011935

Table of Contents

About the Author

Robert E. Owen, M.A.

With more than 15 years of experience, Robert has contributed to the field of education in many capacities, including: teacher (private, public, and alternative), tutor, author, researcher, consultant, and guest lecturer. His curricular and pedagogical perspectives are student-centered, constructivist, and simultaneously challenging and supportive. As an educator, Robert's primary focus is on the advancement of higher-order thinking skills through the development of interdisciplinary curriculum content.

Introduction

Inference Jones improves critical reading and higher-order thinking by developing the students' ability to draw inferences from written text. Research shows inferencing is a prerequisite component for superior reading comprehension. A study by The National Foundation for Educational Research reports that "the ability to draw inferences predetermines reading skills: that is, poor inferencing causes poor comprehension and not vice versa." *Inference Jones* was developed based on this principle.

We all make inferences in our daily lives (for example, we naturally think children are happy because we see them laughing), but how does this ability apply to written communication? When we read a written passage, we're actually reading a representation of the author's thoughts and ideas because the written word does not convey a meaning in and of itself. Readers must construct the meaning through interpretation. They draw from personal knowledge to make inferences based on personal experiences, social values, and cultural conventions. The reader then connects a meaning to the words and makes an inference about a character's actions, circumstances, or events in the story.

Inference Jones: Beginning 2 has a reading level appropriate for Grades 3-4, but it can also be used as a remedial resource for older students up through 12th grade.

Teaching Suggestions

Getting Started

For each activity, read the title out loud and offer students your prediction as to what the story is about. After inviting the students to make predictions of their own, have them explain how they came to their particular interpretation. Continue by reading the story or excerpt, stopping frequently to ask questions.

Transfer From Self to Text

When the reading is finished, try to create an association between an incident from the story (preferably about a character) and something the students can relate to. This dialogical process helps create understanding as the students begin recognizing that their personal experiences affect their interpretation of the text. Once this transfer from self to text is realized, overall comprehension increases and further interpretations and inferences are more easily constructed.

Class Participation

Some students may initially be hesitant to participate in the activities. Keep at it; they generally feel more at ease after they see their classmates participate. Also, although the stories have been designed for the 3rd-4th grade range, not all students will have sufficient experiences to relate to all the events and/or characters.

Specific categories of inferences you'll find in *Inference Jones*:
- Coherence Inference: connecting text
- Elaborative Inference: filling textual gaps
- Global Inference: thematic or moral
- On-line Inference: drawn during reading
- Off-line Inference: drawn after reading

Sample Activity

¹Mike went into the backyard to play on the swing set. ²His new puppy, Rascal, ran beside him. ³As Mike was running toward the play area, he twisted his ankle. ⁴The accident caused him a lot of pain. ⁵Mike's dad was always doing yard work and making sure that the grass was perfectly cut and the ground was even. ⁶Certainly he would have noticed that hole and filled it up. ⁷Neither Mike nor his dad could figure out how the hole appeared.

Circle **T** if you are certain this sentence is true. Circle **F** if you are certain it is false. Circle **U** if it is unknown because you need more information. Add the sentence number(s) on the line that best supports your true or false answer.

The purpose of this set of questions is to enable the student to distinguish between facts and inferences. Facts are stated directly in the story. Inferences require the use of information suggested by the story to draw conclusions.

1. Mike has a new puppy. (T) **2**, F ____, or U

2. Mike cried when he twisted his ankle. T ____, F ____, or (U)

Question number 2 is an inference. The story does not explicitly state that Mike cried, but it can be inferred from sentences 3 and 4 that he might have cried. It is also possible to make an inference based on personal knowledge. Maybe in the past you have cried from painfully twisting your ankle.

Circle the letter next to the correct answer.

The purpose of the second set of questions is to enable students to use higher-order thinking to develop their reading comprehension skills. In this section, you will find a broad array of questions. The comprehension skills that are developed for each activity can be found on page 1. This particular question is cause/effect.

3. What caused Mike to twist his ankle in sentence 3?
    a. his dad
    b. the swing set
    (c.) a hole
    d. none of the above

Which sentence best supports the answer? __**6**__

Circle **PT** for probably true or **PF** for probably false. Be sure to supply the best evidence that supports your answer: sentence number(s) and/or personal knowledge.

The purpose of the third set of questions is to enable students to develop a sense of what is probably true or probably false. After answering, the students are to cite the sentence number(s) for textual evidence or explain how their personal knowledge* led them to making the inference.

4. Mike's dad used a lawn mower to cut the grass.

(PT) or PF   Sentence **5**

Personal knowledge: _I believe this is true because most people I_
Know use a lawn mower to cut their grass.

*Note on Personal Knowledge:

   Maybe you've watched your dad mow the lawn before. If not, maybe you've seen someone use a lawn mower in your neighborhood or on the television. Remember, personal knowledge varies widely from student to student. Personal knowledge-based inferences are informed by historical and cultural contexts. Therefore, different people make different inferences because they bring different past experiences to each story.

SKILLS FOR READING COMPREHENSION & LITERARY ANALYSIS

	Compare/Contrast	Define vocabulary in context	Distinguish cause/effect	Distinguish fact/inference	Draw conclusions	Find supporting evidence	Identify main idea	Make inferences	Make generalizations	Read for details	Use tables, illustrations, etc.	Analyze character traits	Identify theme	Identify setting	Sequence events
READING COMPREHENSION SKILLS												**LITERARY ANALYSIS SKILLS**			
A Friendly Helper	■		■	■	■	■		■		■		■			
My Pet Human		■		■	■	■	■	■		■	■	■			
Liam's Morning			■	■	■	■		■		■	■	■			
The Great Cookie Thief				■	■	■	■	■		■		■			■
It's All Fun Until Someone Gets Hurt	■	■	■	■	■	■		■		■		■			
"Best Teacher in the World"		■	■	■	■	■		■	■	■	■	■			
Coffee Shop Music		■	■	■	■	■		■		■					■
Tiny Tim		■	■	■	■	■		■	■	■				■	
At the Front Door		■	■	■	■	■		■		■					■
Peter and Shanti	■			■	■	■		■		■	■	■	■		
Chris Wouldn't Eat			■	■	■	■		■	■	■		■	■		
Bam!	■			■	■	■		■				■			
Sam Saves the Day				■	■	■		■		■	■			■	■
The Old House		■		■	■	■		■	■	■		■			
Aiden and Reilly				■	■	■	■	■		■		■	■		
Practice and a Good Attitude	■	■		■	■	■		■	■	■		■		■	
Pet Sitting			■	■	■	■		■		■	■	■		■	
Johnny's Cold Feet		■		■	■	■		■		■		■			

1. Johnny's Cold Feet

¹I walked into my room, stubbed my toe on the bed frame, and then slipped on a comic book. ²I hadn't seen that one in months! ³I still had two and a half minutes before my ride to school would arrive. ⁴I just needed a pair of socks, and I'd be ready to go. ⁵I looked in my sock drawer and it was empty. ⁶"Oh, no!" I thought. ⁷I ran to the laundry room and began frantically looking for a matching pair. ⁸HONK! HONK! ⁹I grabbed two socks that I found lying on the laundry room floor, grabbed my backpack, and rushed out the front door. ¹⁰On our way to school I noticed that I had taken my three-year-old brother's socks! ¹¹I came home from school that day with cold, blistered feet.

> Circle **T** if you are certain this sentence is true. Circle **F** if you are certain it is false. Circle **U** if it is unknown because you need more information. Add the sentence number(s) on the line that best supports your true or false answer.

1. Johnny stubbed his toe. T ___, F ___, or U

2. Johnny likes comic books. T ___, F ___, or U

3. Johnny did not run through the family room. T ___, F ___, or U

4. "HONK! HONK!" in sentence 8 was Johnny's ride to school. T ___, F ___, or U

5. Johnny has a three-year-old brother. T ___, F ___, or U

> Write the answer on the lines given or circle the letter next to the correct answer(s).

6. Why did Johnny run to the laundry room?

_____

_____

7. Why did Johnny come home with cold, blistered feet?

_____

_____

8. In sentence 7 infer what "frantically" means.
    a. fearfully
    b. happily
    c. calmly
    d. wildly

9. How is Johnny not feeling in sentence 9?
    a. frantic
    b. relaxed
    c. frustrated
    d. hurried

10. Which sentence best explains that Johnny was in a rush?
    a. 1
    b. 7
    c. 10
    d. 11

Circle **PT** for probably true or **PF** for probably false. Be sure to supply the best evidence that supports your answer: sentence number(s) and/or personal knowledge.

11. Johnny is clumsy.

    PT or PF   Sentence _____

    Personal knowledge: _____

    _____

    _____

12. This story takes place in the morning.

    PT or PF   Sentence _____

    Personal knowledge: _____

    _____

    _____

2. Pet Sitting

¹Pat was pet sitting Cindy's pet bird. ²It was a nice, sunny Saturday morning, so he decided to take a break and go outside to enjoy the sunshine. ³Outside he met his friends, Sharon and Ravi. ⁴They all decided to walk to the park to play basketball. ⁵Halfway through the game, Pat remembered he was supposed to be pet sitting. ⁶He ran as fast as he could back to the house. ⁷As he entered Cindy's house, the neighbor's cat came running out licking his lips. ⁸Pat looked across the family room and saw that the bird was missing from its cage.

> Circle **T** if you are certain this sentence is true. Circle **F** if you are certain it is false. Circle **U** if it is unknown because you need more information. Add the sentence number(s) on the line that best supports your true or false answer.

1. Pat, Ravi, and Sharon played basketball on Saturday. T ___, ___, F ___, or U

2. When Pat returned, the bird was not missing from the cage. T ___, F ___, or U

3. Pat is a girl. T ___, F ___, or U

4. The cat ate the bird. T ___, F ___, or U

> Write the answer on the lines given or circle the letter next to the correct answer(s).

5. Which answer best describes the reason why Pat was watching Cindy's pet bird on Saturday?
   a. Pat liked the bird.
   b. Cindy didn't like birds.
   c. Cindy was on vacation with her family.
   d. none of the above

6. Which word best describes Pat?
   a. mean
   b. smart
   c. forgetful
   d. careful

7. Predict what most likely happened in this story.
     a. The bird flew away.

     b. The cat ate the bird.

     c. Pat was happy.

     d. Sharon ate the bird.

8. What was the earliest cause of Pat's forgetfulness?
     a. the cat

     b. the basketball game

     c. Pat's friends

     d. a nice, sunny morning

9. What can you infer from the picture?

_____

_____

_____

> Circle **PT** for probably true or **PF** for probably false. Be sure to supply the best evidence that supports your answer: sentence number(s) and/or personal knowledge.

10. Cindy trusted Pat.

     PT or PF   Sentence _____

     Personal knowledge: _____

_____

_____

11. The park is not too far from Cindy's house.

     PT or PF   Sentence _____

     Personal knowledge: _____

_____

_____

3. Practice and a Good Attitude

¹As the starting gun was about to sound, I looked over at Jimmy. ²His glowing red eyes stared at me as he smirked. ³His overly confident smile made my stomach churn. ⁴I then looked to my left and saw Mark. ⁵He turned his head away. ⁶Before the race he told me that he never wins at anything, especially running races. ⁷I aimed my head straight ahead, took a deep breath, and felt comfortable and confident that I was going to win. ⁸I had run this track every weekend with my dad since I was 5 years old.

⁹"On your mark."

¹⁰I could hear my dad yelling in the crowd, "You can do it!"

¹¹"Get set." ¹²I knew I could. ¹³"Go!"

¹⁴Jimmy started fast, but I was right on his tail. ¹⁵We rounded the first turn and I decided I needed to pick up the pace. ¹⁶We were running around the track only once, so there wasn't much time. ¹⁷I came up shoulder-to-shoulder with Jimmy. ¹⁸He was bright red, huffing and puffing. ¹⁹I couldn't believe it, I wasn't even tired yet. ²⁰I easily passed Jimmy, and after I did, I looked back to see Mark passing him, too! ²¹As I approached the finish line, the crowd was cheering. ²²Then the score board lit up the words: "A New School Record for the Quarter Mile!" ²³Mark came in with a big smile and gave me a high five. ²⁴Jimmy sat down, moping. ²⁵He couldn't believe he was beaten by a girl who was two years younger than he was. ²⁶I looked over at my dad, and I knew he was proud.

> Circle **T** if you are certain this sentence is true. Circle **F** if you are certain it is false. Circle **U** if it is unknown because you need more information. Add the sentence number(s) on the line that best supports your true or false answer.

1. The narrator is 7 years old. T ____, F ____, or U

2. The race was a quarter mile long. T ____, F ____, or U

3. Mark was scared before the race. T ____, F ____, or U

> Circle the letter next to the correct answers.

4. In sentence 2 infer what "smirked" means.
   a. closed his eyes
   b. winked
   c. half-smiled
   d. frowned

5. This story most likely did not take place:
   a. in a stadium.
   b. on a school track.
   c. outside.
   d. in a classroom.

6. Who or what helped the narrator win the race?
   a. Jimmy
   b. practice and confidence
   c. luck
   d. secret powers

7. Compare Mark's personality to Jimmy's.
   a. glad; overconfident
   b. overconfident; not confident
   c. overconfident; glad
   d. not confident; overconfident

8. What can you reasonably infer from reading sentences 2 and 3?
   a. Jimmy was fast.
   b. Mark was a good swimmer.
   c. Jimmy was older than Mark and the narrator.
   d. Jimmy thought he was going to win.

Circle **PT** for probably true or **PF** for probably false. Be sure to supply the best evidence that supports your answer: sentence number(s) and/or personal knowledge.

9. This was an organized school event and attended by many people.

PT or PF   Sentences _____ _____

Personal knowledge: _____

_____

_____

10. Jimmy had never been beaten in a running race by a younger girl.

PT or PF   Sentence _____

Personal knowledge: _____

_____

_____

4. Aiden and Reilly

¹Aiden and Reilly lived together in the snow. ²In fact, they were snowmen!   ³Aiden was younger than Reilly. ⁴He always did whatever he felt like doing. ⁵Aiden wore a metal bucket on his head, while Reilly did not. ⁶Aiden also liked to throw snowballs at the birds. ⁷Reilly never liked when he did this. ⁸He always tried to protect his neighbors in the forest.

⁹One day, Aiden asked Reilly if he wanted to go for a walk. ¹⁰Reilly declined the offer, and then he reminded Aiden about what the other snowmen always said: "Don't go past the Great Meadow." ¹¹He told Aiden that it gets very warm beyond the meadow, and it would be dangerous for him to go there. ¹²Aiden turned away without listening and began walking. ¹³He arrived at the Great Meadow, stopped, and then kept on walking. ¹⁴Reilly never saw Aiden again.

> Circle **T** if you are certain this sentence is true. Circle **F** if you are certain it is false. Circle **U** if it is unknown because you need more information. Add the sentence number(s) on the line that best supports your true or false answer.

1. Aiden is older than Reilly. T ___, F ___, or U

2. Aiden and Reilly live in the city. T ___, F ___, or U

3. Aiden wore a wooden bucket on his head. T ___, F ___, or U

> Write the answer on the lines given or circle the letter next to the correct answer(s).

4. What probably happened to Aiden? Write the number of the sentence that best supports your answer.

_____

_____

_____

Best evidence sentence: _____

5. What is the point of this story?
   a. Don't play in the snow.
   b. Being reckless can be dangerous.
   c. Snowmen talk to each other when people aren't around.
   d. Sun melts snow.

6. Which statements can you reasonably conclude from sentence 8?
   a. Reilly would save a skunk from freezing in the snow.
   b. Aiden would help a wounded hawk.
   c. Reilly would make a good hunter.
   d. Aiden would help a baby bear in trouble.

7. Aiden's and Reilly's character traits are:
   a. the same.
   b. almost alike.
   c. different.
   d. similar.

8. Which could be a different title for this story?
   a. Two Polar Snowmen
   b. A Winter in Mexico
   c. Frosty's Children
   d. The Snowman Who Wouldn't Listen

Circle **PT** for probably true or **PF** for probably false. Be sure to supply the best evidence that supports your answer: sentence number(s) and/or personal knowledge.

9. Aiden walked past the Great Meadow and melted.

   PT or PF   Sentences _____ _____ _____

   Personal knowledge: _____

   _____

   _____

10. The two snowmen lived near a forest.

   PT or PF   Sentence _____

   Personal knowledge: _____

   _____

   _____

5. The Old House

¹Everyone always stayed away from the old red and yellow house on the corner of our block.   ²Some people said that a mean old woman lived there.   ³Others claimed that they had seen a man on the porch surrounded by hundreds of cats.   ⁴Sometimes on the way home from school, my best friend, Jason, would sneak up to the house, ring the doorbell, and run.   ⁵Well, one windy day, Jason quietly tiptoed up to the front door and accidentally stepped on a squeaky board on the front porch.   ⁶He stopped, looked at me, and then took a few more steps toward the doorbell.   ⁷SWOOSH!!!   ⁸The screen door swung open and slammed hard against the front wall of the house.   ⁹Jason froze; he didn't move a muscle.   ¹⁰The rest of us ran down the street as fast as our feet could take us.

> Circle **T** if you are certain this sentence is true. Circle **F** if you are certain it is false. Circle **U** if it is unknown because you need more information. Add the sentence number(s) on the line that best supports your true or false answer.

1.   Jason saw the mean, old woman. T ____, F ____, or U

2.   It was a windy day. T ____, F ____, or U

3.   The old house is not blue. T ____, F ____, or U

> Write the answer on the lines given or circle the letter next to the correct answer(s).

4.   Give at least 2 reasons why the screen door could have swung open.

_____

_____

_____

5.   Which two words best describe Jason's character?
    a. furious, funny
    b. disrespectful, uncaring
    c. polite, generous
    d. kind, patient

6. In sentence 9, infer what "froze" means.
    a. He stopped.
    b. He got cold.
    c. He turned into an ice cube.
    d. none of the above

7. Which best describes the kind of story this is?
    a. non-fiction
    b. fairy tale
    c. comedy
    d. mystery/suspense

Circle **PT** for probably true or **PF** for probably false. Be sure to supply the best evidence that supports your answer: sentence number(s) and/or personal knowledge.

8. The group of kids didn't get scared when the screen door swung open.

    PT or PF   Sentence _____

    Personal knowledge: _____

    _____

    _____

9. This story happened on a Saturday morning.

    PT or PF   Sentence _____

    Personal knowledge: _____

    _____

    _____

6. Sam Saves the Day

[1]I watched as Ben the Bully walked up to little Timmy's table. [2]Timmy was quietly having lunch as usual. [3]He was reading his favorite comic book when Ben approached him and tore the book right out of his hands. [4]Timmy was so terrified he couldn't even look up at Ben's angry eyes. [5]Just as Timmy was about to stand up and run, his big brother, Sumo Sam, walked into the school cafeteria. [6]The whole room went quiet. [7]Even Chatty Kathy stopped talking. [8]Timmy smiled and took a deep breath. [9]He knew everything was going to be okay.

> Circle **T** if you are certain this sentence is true. Circle **F** if you are certain it is false. Circle **U** if it is unknown because you need more information. Add the sentence number(s) on the line that best supports your true or false answer.

1. Timmy and Sam are brothers. T ____, F ____, or U

2. The story takes place in the school cafeteria. T ____, F ____, or U

3. Chatty Kathy is related to Timmy. T ____, F ____, or U

> Write the answer on the lines given or circle the letter next to the correct answer(s).

4. Why did Timmy smile and take a deep breath?

   _____

   _____

   _____

5. Timmy's feelings change throughout the story. Which three words best describe the sequence of Timmy's feelings?
   a. excited, loved, nervous
   b. loved, nervous, scared
   c. good, scared, relieved
   d. relieved, scared, nervous

6. Who is the main character of this story?
    a. the narrator
    b. Timmy
    c. Sam
    d. Ben

7. Who is telling the story?
    a. Timmy
    b. someone who saw what happened
    c. Chatty Kathy
    d. Ben

8. Number these events in order.
    _____ a. Chatty Kathy stopped talking.
    _____ b. Timmy Smiled.
    _____ c. Ben took Timmy's comic book.
    _____ d. Sumo Sam walked into the cafeteria.

Circle **PT** for probably true or **PF** for probably false. Be sure to supply the best evidence that supports your answer: sentence number(s) and/or personal knowledge.

9. The whole room went quiet because they wanted to see what was going to happen.

    PT or PF   Sentence _____

    Personal knowledge: _____

    _____

    _____

10. Looking at the picture on page 12, the bigger boy is Ben the Bully.

    PT or PF   Sentence _____

    Personal knowledge: _____

    _____

    _____

7. BAM!

¹Aleah and Jenna were up late watching a movie at Jenna's house when they heard a loud BAM! ²They looked at each other, then quickly jumped up and ran to the window. ³Their hearts were racing. ⁴They saw the taillights of what could have been an old pickup truck driving away. ⁵Aleah went back to watch the movie, but Jenna decided to go outside and find out more about what caused the loud sound. ⁶Jenna put on her snow boots and walked through the deep snow to find a dent in her dad's brand new car. ⁷She ran back inside to find Aleah asleep with an empty bowl of popcorn at her feet.

> Circle **T** if you are certain this sentence is true. Circle **F** if you are certain it is false. Circle **U** if it is unknown because you need more information. Add the sentence number(s) on the line that best supports your true or false answer.

1. Both girls heard a loud "BAM!" T _____, F _____, or U

2. The girls were playing games on the computer when they heard the

    loud sound. T _____, F _____, or U

3. Jenna's dad's car had a dent in it. T _____, F _____, or U

4. Jenna was cold when she walked outside that night. T _____, F _____, or U

> Write the answer on the lines given or circle the letter next to the correct answer(s).

5. What did Jenna do differently from Aleah after they both saw the taillights of the pickup truck drive away?

    _____

    _____

    _____

6. Which sentences provide the best evidence that the pickup truck may have hit Jenna's dad's car?
    a. 3, 6
    b. 3, 4
    c. 1, 4, 6
    d. 2, 4, 7

7. What is the best inference that could be made from sentence 7?
    a. Aleah was not tired.
    b. Aleah likes movies.
    c. Aleah was tired and likes popcorn.
    d. Jenna was angry.

8. In sentence 3 infer what "racing" means.
    a. competing
    b. winning a race
    c. stopping
    d. moving quickly

Circle **PT** for probably true or **PF** for probably false. Be sure to supply the best evidence that supports your answer: sentence number(s) and/or personal knowledge.

9. The truck hit Jenna's dad's car on purpose.

    PT or PF   Sentence _____

    Personal knowledge: _____

    _____

    _____

10. Aleah likes popcorn.

    PT or PF   Sentence _____

    Personal knowledge: _____

    _____

    _____

8. Chris Wouldn't Eat

[1]My best friend Chris couldn't come over after school today. [2]We were at lunch and he was afraid to eat anything. [3]I offered him an apple, a carrot, and even a candy cane, but he wouldn't take them today. [4]I knew something was wrong. [5]When we went to class after the lunch break he was extra quiet and looked very pale. [6]When the teacher called on him, he stood up and ran out of the classroom. [7]He came back about 10 minutes later rubbing his stomach. [8]I wondered why he was acting so strange.

> Circle **T** if you are certain this sentence is true. Circle **F** if you are certain it is false. Circle **U** if it is unknown because you need more information. Add the sentence number(s) on the line that best supports your true or false answer.

1. Chris would not eat a sandwich during lunch. T ___, F ___, or U

2. The narrator felt sad for Chris. T ___, F ___, or U

3. Chris went to the bathroom for a tissue. T ___, F ___, or U

4. It was Chris's worst day at school. T ___, F ___, or U

> Circle the letter next to the correct answer(s).

5. What probably caused Chris to act different that day?
    a. Chris had a nosebleed.
    b. Chris was sad.
    c. Chris was not feeling well.
    d. Chris was upset that the teacher called on him.

6. How does the narrator feel about Chris?
    a. angry that Chris can't come over
    b. frustrated that Chris didn't eat a candy cane
    c. curious about Chris's behavior
    d. jealous that Chris missed 10 minutes of class

7. This story most likely took place around:
    a. 6:00 a.m.
    b. 8:15 a.m.
    c. 8:15 p.m.
    d. 12:00 p.m.

8. What most likely caused Chris to miss the 10 minutes of class?
    a. He was hungry.
    b. He was sad.
    c. He had a hair appointment.
    d. none of the above

Circle **PT** for probably true or **PF** for probably false. Be sure to supply the best evidence that supports your answer: sentence number(s) and/or personal knowledge.

9. By the end of class, Chris's teacher knew something was wrong with Chris.

    PT or PF   Sentence _____

    Personal knowledge: _____

    _____

10. Chris ran out of the room because he wasn't feeling well.

    PT or PF   Sentences ____ ____ ____ ____ ____ ____ ____

    Personal knowledge: _____

    _____

    _____

11. Chris usually eats some lunch.

    PT or PF   Sentences ____ ____ ____

    Personal knowledge: _____

    _____

    _____

9. Peter and Shanti

[1]Peter is in the fourth grade and lives on a peaceful farm in Lexington, Kentucky. [2]His parents have been homeschooling him since he was five years old. [3]Every morning, after enjoying two scrambled eggs and a half piece of toast, he sits down to read the local newspaper. [4]Although he doesn't understand everything he reads, he always does his best. [5]His mom asks him to circle ten words he doesn't know and to write three questions he has about any article he chooses. [6]He begins his science lesson for the day once he completes his morning newspaper activity.

[7]Shanti lives in the bustling city of New Delhi, India. [8]Every morning her mom cooks Shanti her favorite breakfast, egg dosa. [9]After Shanti finishes her meal, she leaves her apartment, walks across the busy street, and waits for the bus. [10]The bus then takes her to school where she learns about math, science, English, and history. [11]When the dismissal bell rings, Shanti runs to the bus stop.

> Circle **T** if you are certain this sentence is true. Circle **F** if you are certain it is false. Circle **U** if it is unknown because you need more information. Add the sentence number(s) on the line that best supports your true or false answer.

1. Shanti lives in India. T ____, F ____, or U

2. Peter understands everything he reads in the newspaper. T ____, F ____, or U

3. Shanti and Peter are both in the 4th grade. T ____, F ____, or U

> Write the answer on the lines given or circle the letter next to the correct answer(s).

4. Identify at least three similarities between Peter and Shanti. Write the sentence numbers that support the answer.

   _____

   _____

   _____

   _____

5. What can you predict from sentence 11?
    a. The bus will come to take Shanti home.

    b. Shanti will study math.

    c. Shanti will drive the bus home.

    d. Shanti will share her egg dosa with the bus driver.

6. Which of the following is not true about the lives of Shanti and Peter.
    a. Shanti is a girl and Peter is a boy.

    b. Peter and Shanti are homeschooled.

    c. Peter lives on a farm and Shanti lives in the city.

    d. Shanti lives in India and Peter lives in Kentucky.

7. Which sentences best support this statement: "The area in New Delhi where Shanti lives is highly populated"?
    a. 9, 10

    b. 3, 4

    c. 7, 10

    d. 7, 9

8. What is wrong with this picture of Peter's homeschool experience?

    _____

    _____

    _____

    _____

Circle **PT** for probably true or **PF** for probably false. Be sure to supply the best evidence that supports your answer: sentence number(s) and/or personal knowledge.

9. Peter's farm is quieter during the day than Shanti's neighborhood.

    PT or PF   Sentences _____ _____ _____

    Personal knowledge: _____

    _____

    _____

10. At the Front Door

¹Knock, knock, knock. ²There was someone at the front door. ³Mom had just run out to the grocery store and would be right back. ⁴Hmmm … Should I answer it? ⁵No, I think I'll ignore it. ⁶Knock, knock, knock. ⁷Knock, knock, knock. ⁸Man, this person was persistent. ⁹I quietly crept to the front window next to the calendar marked October 31 and almost tripped over a bowl of candy. ¹⁰ All I could see was a red cape with the letter "S" on it. ¹¹Oh, wow! ¹²It was Superman! ¹³I could barely hold in my excitement. ¹⁴I grabbed the doorknob and turned it, but it didn't open. ¹⁵So I released the deadbolt, swung open the door, and … he was gone. ¹⁶The only thing he left on the porch was a candy wrapper. ¹⁷He must have flown back to Metropolis. ¹⁸Even Superman has to be home in time for dinner.

Circle **T** if you are certain this sentence is true. Circle **F** if you are certain it is false. Circle **U** if it is unknown because you need more information. Add the sentence number(s) on the line that best supports your true or false answer.

1. The narrator saw a red cape. T ____, F ____, or U

2. This person is home alone. T ____, F ____, or U

3. The narrator's mom was out shopping for dinner. T ____, F ____, or U

Circle the letter next to the correct answer(s).

4. In sentence 8 infer what "persistent" means.
    a. angry
    b. forgiving
    c. determined
    d. smart

5. Which sentences best support the notion that this story took place on the night some people celebrate Halloween?
    a. 4, 5
    b. 6, 7
    c. 8, 9
    d. 9, 10

6. Why did the narrator think the person at the door was Superman?
   Circle the best answer.
   a. The person at the door wore a red cape.

   b. The cape had the letter "S" on it.

   c. The narrator forgot that it was Halloween.

   d. all of the above

7. Number these events in order.
   _____ a. An empty candy wrapper was found on the front porch.

   _____ b. Someone came to the front door.

   _____ c. The narrator saw the red cape.

   _____ d. The narrator unlocked the deadbolt and swung open the door.

Circle **PT** for probably true or **PF** for probably false. Be sure to supply the best evidence that supports your answer: sentence number(s) and/or personal knowledge.

8. The narrator didn't answer the door at first because his mom was not home.

   PT or PF   Sentence _____

   Personal knowledge: _____

   _____

   _____

9. The narrator is 10 years old or younger.

   PT or PF   Sentence _____

   Personal knowledge: _____

   _____

   _____

11. Tiny Tim

[1]I felt a little strange after Professor Shrinky Dink pulled the trigger on his new, mysterious laser gun. [2]I found myself running from huge flies, oversized ants, and giant bees. [3]To escape, I ran across a checkerboard cloth, climbed over a pool wall, and jumped into the red water. [4]It seemed as though I was invulnerable at that moment, so I just swam around and enjoyed the taste of this giant swimming pool. [5]The next instant I was swept up into a spoon and then dumped into a small glass. [6]Luckily, I was able to climb on top of the ice cubes and get out of there. [7]I ran around looking for another hiding place and found one next to an enormous peanut butter and jelly sandwich. [8]I fell asleep waiting to return to reality. [9]When I awoke I was back in the professor's kitchen, and he was shaking me saying, "Tim, Tim, wake up."

Circle **T** if you are certain this sentence is true. Circle **F** if you are certain it is false. Circle **U** if it is unknown because you need more information. Add the sentence number(s) on the line that best supports your true or false answer.

1. Professor Shrinky Dink has a laser gun. T ____, F ____, or U

2. Tim was shrunk to 5 inches tall. T ____, F ____, or U

3. Tiny Tim swam in a bowl of Kool-Aid. T ____, F ____, or U

Write the answer on the lines given or circle the letter next to the correct answer(s).

4. What do you think the pool was?

_____

_____

_____

5. How would you classify this story?
    a. non-fiction
    b. history
    c. action
    d. drama

6. What can you infer from sentence 1?
   a. Tim liked Kool-Aid.

   b. Tim is a scientist.

   c. Professor Shrinky Dink is a scientist.

   d. Professor Shrinky Dink doesn't like sandwiches.

7. In sentence 4 infer what "invulnerable" means.
   a. safe

   b. in danger

   c. petrified

   d. horrible

8. What caused Tim to jump into the red pool of water?
   a. the laser gun

   b. flies, ants, and tigers

   c. flies, ants, and bees

   d. lions, tigers, and bears

9. Circle the picture to the right that best relates to the story. Explain your answer.

a.   b.    c.

_____

_____

_____

Circle **PT** for probably true or **PF** for probably false. Be sure to supply the best evidence that supports your answer: sentence number(s) and/or personal knowledge.

10. This story took place in Professor Shrinky Dink's home.

    PT or PF   Sentence _____

    Personal knowledge: _____

    _____

    _____

12. Coffee Shop Music

¹Sid was sitting in Joe's Café waiting for the next band to play. ²He looked over and noticed a group of guys setting up musical equipment. ³He couldn't help noticing that some of the musicians had long hair. ⁴Although this didn't bother him, he wondered why a guy would grow his hair long. ⁵He then began thinking about all the girls he knew with short hair and wondered if this was just as different as guys with long hair.

⁶After about 15 minutes, he was about to leave when a guy with black boots, jeans, a T-shirt, and long hair sat one table over from him. ⁷Sid paused, then leaned over and asked the man when his band was going to start playing. ⁸The man looked over, perplexed. ⁹The man told Sid that he wasn't in the band.

> Circle **T** if you are certain this sentence is true. Circle **F** if you are certain it is false. Circle **U** if it is unknown because you need more information. Add the sentence number(s) on the line that best supports your true or false answer.

1. Some of the musicians had long hair. T ____, F ____, or U

2. Sid thinks most musicians have long hair. T ____, F ____, or U

3. Sid is the man in the picture. T ____, F ____, or U

> Circle the letter next to the correct answer(s).

4. Number these events in order.
    _____ a. Sid was sitting at Joe's Café.
    _____ b. The man looked perplexed.
    _____ c. Sid noticed a band setting up.
    _____ d. Sid spoke to the man.

5. What was the man at the end of the story wearing?
    a. black shorts and jacket
    b. black jacket and hat
    c. blue suspenders and cap
    d. none of the above

6. In sentence 8 infer what "perplexed" means.
    a. disturbed
    b. confused
    c. furious
    d. challenged

7. What caused Sid to think the man was in a band?
    a. The man had a guitar.
    b. The man had black boots and jeans.
    c. The man had long hair.
    d. none of the above

8. Which sentence is the best evidence that Sid wanted to hear some music?
    a. 2
    b. 8
    c. 6
    d. 1

9. Why do you think Sid asked the man with long hair when his band was going to start playing?
    a. This coffee shop has bands every Saturday.
    b. He assumed the man played in the band.
    c. Sid had a plane to catch.
    d. Sid wanted to dance.

Circle **PT** for probably true or **PF** for probably false. Be sure to supply the best evidence that supports your answer: sentence number(s) and/or personal knowledge.

10. Sid thinks guys should have short hair.

    PT or PF   Sentence _____

    Personal knowledge: _____

    _____

    _____

    _____

13. The Best Teacher in the World

¹Emily's mom is a teacher. ²She no longer works in the classroom, but she still loves to teach. ³She has been homeschooling Emily since Emily was 4 years old. ⁴They start school right after feeding the chickens and milking the cows. ⁵Emily usually sits down to enjoy a bowl of cereal while working on the subject of her choice. ⁶After completing her first lesson, she begins with the second. ⁷Emily's mom, Lisa, requires Emily to do four lessons a day: two in the morning and two in the afternoon. ⁸Sometimes Emily is done with her school work by 2:00 p.m., other days not until 5:00 p.m. ⁹One day at lunchtime, Emily was outside running after her dog and she fell down. ¹⁰Her knee began to bleed. ¹¹She was fine until she saw the blood, then she let out an ear-piercing scream. ¹²Her mom came running, calmly picked her up, and carried her inside. ¹³After she bandaged up Emily's knee, it was time for schoolwork again. ¹⁴She walked into the kitchen and on the table were two peanut butter cookies, a tall glass of milk, and her reading lesson for the day. ¹⁵Emily smiled; she knew that she had the best teacher in the world.

> Circle **T** if you are certain this sentence is true. Circle **F** if you are certain it is false. Circle **U** if it is unknown because you need more information. Add the sentence number(s) on the line that best supports your true or false answer.

1. Lisa does not teach in a classroom anymore. T ____, F ____, or U

2. Emily is expected to finish four lessons per day. T ____, F ____, or U

3. Emily scraped her knee before 5:00 p.m.

  T ____ ____ ____ ____ , F ____ ____ ____ ____, or U

> Circle the letter next to the correct answer(s).

4. What caused Emily to scream?
  a. running after her dog
  b. the sight of blood
  c. a long fall
  d. none of the above

5. Which sentence best supports the argument that Emily's mom is also her teacher?

    a. 1

    b. 12

    c. 13

    d. 3

6. Which sentence would best summarize this story?

    a. Emily's homeschool day is with her favorite teacher, her mom.

    b. Emily skins her knee.

    c. Learning should be done in school.

    d. Four lessons a day keeps the doctor away.

Circle **PT** for probably true or **PF** for probably false. Be sure to supply the best evidence that supports your answer: sentence number(s) and/or personal knowledge.

7. You would find chicken feed and fresh milk at Emily's house.

    PT or PF   Sentence _____

    Personal knowledge: _____

    _____

    _____

8. Emily puts milk on her cereal before she eats it.

    PT or PF   Sentence _____

    Personal knowledge: _____

    _____

    _____

14. It's All Fun Until Someone Gets Hurt

¹The bell rang and Andre sat down next to Chris. ²It was time for art class to begin. ³Mr. Penny walked in, put a box of art supplies down, and then began introducing the lesson for the day. ⁴Once he finished his short talk on primary and secondary colors, the class began drawing. ⁵After about 5 minutes, Chris raised his hand and told Mr. Penny he was done with his work. ⁶Although Mr. Penny suggested Chris work a little more on his drawing, Chris didn't listen. ⁷He sat staring at the wall for about 5 minutes before he started feeling mischievous. ⁸He wanted to cause some trouble, but in a playful way. ⁹A few minutes later, Chris noticed Mr. Penny had stepped out of the classroom and that Andre had finished drawing and was deep in a book for class. ¹⁰So he stood up, acted like he dropped his pencil next to Andre's feet, and then tied Andre's shoelaces together. ¹¹A couple of the students chuckled, while others showed a look of concern on their faces.

> Circle **T** if you are certain this sentence is true. Circle **F** if you are certain it is false. Circle **U** if it is unknown because you need more information. Add the sentence number(s) on the line that best supports your true or false answer.

1. Andre and Chris sit in the back of the class. T ___, F ___, or U

2. Andre had finished his assignment before Chris tied his shoelaces.

   T ___ ___, F ___ ___, or U

3. Chris sat down next to Andre. T ___, F ___, or U

4. Mr. Penny told Chris to stare at the wall. T ___, F ___, or U

> Write the answer on the lines given or circle the letter next to the correct answer(s).

5. What probably happened to Andre after Chris tied his shoelaces together?

   _____

   _____

   _____

6. Based on the story, what is wrong with the picture on page 28?

_____

_____

_____

7. Which sentence best provides evidence that the other students in the class
    had mixed feelings about Chris's action?
    a. 1
    b. 6
    c. 5
    d. none of the above

8. In sentence 7, infer what "mischievous" means.
    a. honest and playful

    b. mean but careful

    c. troublesome and playful

    d. careless but mean

9. What effect did the feeling of mischievousness have on Chris? It caused him to:
    a. raise his hand.

    b. not listen to the teacher.

    c. stare at the wall.

    d. tie Andre's laces together.

Circle **PT** for probably true or **PF** for probably false. Be sure to supply the best
evidence that supports your answer: sentence number(s) and/or personal knowledge.

10. Mr. Penny carries pencils, paintbrushes, markers, and art paper to his class.

PT or PF   Sentence _____

Personal knowledge: _____

_____

_____

15. The Great Cookie Thief

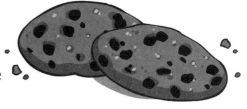

¹Last night my whole family made chocolate chip cookies, my little brother's favorite. ²When we were done, we cleaned up the kitchen, and then I went to watch a movie. ³After the movie was over, and my little brother had gone to bed, I peeked into the kitchen. ⁴I saw a little mouse in the cabinet above the freshly baked cookies. ⁵I turned off the kitchen light and went to bed. ⁶When I came downstairs in the morning, I noticed a small piece of a cookie was missing, and a few crumbs next to the plate. ⁷I couldn't believe my little brother would do that!

> Circle **T** if you are certain this sentence is true. Circle **F** if you are certain it is false. Circle **U** if it is unknown because you need more information. Add the sentence number(s) on the line that best supports your true or false answer.

1. The narrator is the oldest brother in the family. T ____, F ____, or U

2. The mouse ate the cookie. T ____, F ____, or U

3. The kitchen is downstairs from the narrator's room. T ____, F ____, or U

> Write the answer on the lines given or circle the letter next to the correct answer(s).

4. At the end of the story, the narrator thinks:
    a. The mouse ate the cookie.
    b. The parents ate the cookie.
    c. The Cookie Monster ate the cookie.
    d. His little brother ate the cookie.

5. Why might the narrator think that the little brother ate the cookie?

    _____

    _____

    _____

    _____

6. Number these events in order.

_____ a. Part of a cookie was found missing.

_____ b. The family made cookies.

_____ c. The narrator saw a mouse.

_____ d. The narrator watched a movie.

7. The main idea of this story could be:

a. Someone or something ate part of a baked cookie.

b. Someone ate the whole cookie.

c. The little brother likes cookies.

d. The mouse likes cookies.

8. There would be no mystery:

a. without the missing piece of cookie.

b. if the little brother did not like chocolate chip cookies.

c. if there was no mouse in the story.

d. all of the above

Circle **PT** for probably true or **PF** for probably false. Be sure to supply the best evidence that supports your answer: sentence number(s) and/or personal knowledge.

9. The narrator is not afraid of mice.

PT or PF   Sentences _____ _____

Personal knowledge: _____

_____

_____

10. The narrator's little brother ate the cookie.

PT or PF   Sentences _____ _____ _____

Personal knowledge: _____

_____

_____

16. Liam's Morning

¹Peter Gabriel's hit song blasted through Liam's digital alarm clock. ²It was 7:15 a.m. and time for school. ³After rubbing his tired eyes, he got up, turned off the clock radio, and put on his Spiderman slippers.   ⁴*The Book of Beginnings,* one of his favorite books, caught his eye, so he grabbed it and sat down on the floor. ⁵He thumbed through the pages looking at all of the interesting pictures. ⁶While reading about the inventor of the first complex water clock, Yi Xing (683-727), he began to smell bacon. ⁷He quickly jumped up and ran downstairs. ⁸His mom had just finished cooking him a bacon, egg, and cheese scramble.

> Circle **T** if you are certain this sentence is true. Circle **F** if you are certain it is false. Circle **U** if it is unknown because you need more information. Add the sentence number(s) on the line that best supports your true or false answer.

1. Liam likes Spiderman. T ____, F ____, or U

2. Liam lives in a two-story house. T ____, F ____, or U

3. *The Book of Beginnings* is Liam's favorite book. T ____, F ____, or U

> Write the answer on the lines given or circle the letters next to the correct answer(s).

4. Identify 3 elements in the story that are not included in the picture above.

    _____

    _____

    _____

5. Which sentence best proves that Liam's mom was cooking bacon?
    a. 6
    b. 4
    c. 8
    d. none of the above

6. What caused Liam to run downstairs?
    a. *The Book of Beginnings*

    b. his dad calling his name

    c. the smell of bacon

    d. the smell of pancakes

7. What do you think Liam will do next?
    a. go to school

    b. eat, then go back to bed

    c. eat, then go to school

    d. go to school, then eat

8. Number these events in order.

    _____a. Liam ran downstairs.

    _____b. It turned 7:15 a.m.

    _____c. Liam rubbed his eyes and got up.

    _____d. Liam read about Yi Xing.

Circle **PT** for probably true or **PF** for probably false. Be sure to supply the best evidence that supports your answer: sentence number(s) and/or personal knowledge.

9. Liam is 2 years old.

    PT or PF   Sentence _____

    Personal knowledge: _____

    _____

    _____

10. Liam does not enjoy reading.

    PT or PF   Sentences _____ _____

    Personal knowledge: _____

    _____

    _____

17. My Pet Human

[1]Wow, it sure is cold in this big house! [2]I wonder where my human went. [3]Oh, there she is, tapping on those buttons again. [4]I think I'll go and jump on them to annoy her a bit. [5]It's so fun to watch her reaction, plus she usually feeds me after I distract her from staring at that computer screen all day. [6]Click, Click. [7]"HEY! GET OFF THERE, SYLVESTER!" [8]That'll do it. [9]Now I'll just hop off this chair, onto the floor, and walk in circles until she comes around the corner. [10]Here she comes. [11]I bet I can beat her to the kitchen. [12]Yup, every time. [13]It must be tough having only two legs. [14]I'm starving; I wish she didn't take so long fixing my food. [15]Finally! Yes! [16]Sardines and salmon are my favorite!

[17]Mmmm … that was great. [18]Now, if I can only get her to swing around that plastic mouse for me to chase. [19]PRRR … PRRRR ….

[20]"Syl, do you want to play with little mousy?" [21]Yes, I knew I could keep her from tapping those buttons again. [22]Oh, yea, swing it again and again! [23]I love the taste of this little mousy. [24]Ok, I'm tired now. [25]I think I'll rest in her lap and snuggle until I decide that I need something else from her. [26]I love my pet human.

> Circle **T** if you are certain this sentence is true. Circle **F** if you are certain it is false. Circle **U** if it is unknown because you need more information. Add the sentence number(s) on the line that best supports your true or false answer.

1. The human's name is not Cindy. T ____, F ____, or U

2. The house is cold. T ____, F ____, or U

3. Sylvester does not consider himself a pet. T ____, F ____, or U

> Write the answer on the lines given or circle the letter next to the correct answer(s).

4. Explain why the picture above does not work with the story.

   _____

   _____

   _____

5. Describe Sylvester's personality.
   a. loving and kind
   b. scared and fearful
   c. brave and courageous
   d. playful and spoiled

6. Which sentence(s) best supports the idea that Sylvester is not a dog?
   a. 13
   b. 19.
   c. 4.
   d. 26.

7. What is the main idea of this story?
   a. Sylvester likes sardines and salmon.
   b. The human and cat have changed roles.
   c. Humans are smarter than cats.
   d. Sylvester keeps his human from watching television.

8. What probably happened in-between these two sentences: "Oh, yea, swing it again and again! I love the taste of this little mousy."
   a. The human swung the bowl.
   b. The human was annoyed.
   c. Sylvester caught the mouse and put it in his mouth.
   d. Sylvester jumped on the computer mouse.

Circle **PT** for probably true or **PF** for probably false. Be sure to supply the best evidence that supports your answer: sentence number(s) and/or personal knowledge.

9. Sylvester is a cat.

   PT or PF   Sentences _____ _____ _____

   Personal knowledge: _____

   _____

10. Sylvester distracts his human from the computer.

   PT or PF   Sentence _____

   Personal knowledge: _____

   _____

18. A Friendly Helper

¹Farah's family had just finished moving in when they heard a knock at the door. ²Standing there was a young, blonde-haired girl about her age. ³They both said, "Hi," at the same time, and then giggled. ⁴The girl asked if Farah could come out and play. ⁵Farah looked at her parents and they both nodded happily, yes. ⁶The girls ran off to the park. ⁷While they were running, the blonde-haired girl turned and yelled, "My name is Jenny, what's yours?"

⁸In between breaths, Farah moved her curly, dark hair and yelled, "Farah!"

⁹They arrived at the park and came upon a small group of girls playing soccer. ¹⁰Farah was a really good softball player in her old neighborhood, but had never played soccer.

¹¹"Hey, wanna play?" yelled one of the soccer players.

¹²Both girls replied with a loud, "YES!"

¹³ The teams were already even in numbers, so Farah and Jenny joined opposing teams. ¹⁴Farah then became a little scared because she didn't know the rules. ¹⁵The excitement stirred in Jenny; she hadn't played since last season. ¹⁶The whistle blew. ¹⁷The girls began kicking the ball around toward the goal, but when the ball came to Farah, she picked it up and threw it. ¹⁸Everyone laughed except Jenny. ¹⁹Jenny kindly explained to her neighborhood friends that Farah did not know the rules. ²⁰The whistle blew and the game began again. ²¹Farah stood there and watched as the players passed the ball back and forth. ²²Suddenly, the ball came right at her chest and without thinking, she put up her hands and knocked it down to the ground. ²³The whistle blew. ²⁴Her face became flushed and it looked like she was about to cry. ²⁵Jenny ran over to her new friend and suggested she play goalie. ²⁶After Jenny explained to Farah that the goalie can catch the ball, Farah was happy to play. ²⁷Right before the game was about to end, Jenny came dribbling down the field as fast as lightning. ²⁸Not a single player was near her. ²⁹It was now up to Farah to save the winning goal against Jenny. ³⁰Jenny shot the ball and Farah dove to the upper corner of the goal, knocking it out of play. ³¹Both teams celebrated a great game.

Circle **T** if you are certain this sentence is true. Circle **F** if you are certain it is false. Circle **U** if it is unknown because you need more information. Add the sentence number(s) on the line that best supports your true or false answer.

1. Farah moved next door to Jenny. T ___, F ___, or U

2. Farah and Jenny became friends. T ___, F ___, or U

3. Jenny knew the group of girls playing soccer. T ___, F ___, or U